SOCCER:

It's A Funny Old Game

SOCCER:

It's A Funny Old Game

David Langdon

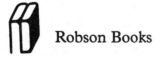
Robson Books

To all at Wycombe Wanderers F.C.

First published in Great Britain in 1998 by Robson Books Ltd,
Bolsover House, 5-6 Clipstone Street, London W1P 8LE

Copyright © 1998 David Langdon
The right of David Langdon to be identified as author of this work has
been asserted by him in accordance with the Copyright, Designs and
Patents Act 1988

British Library Cataloguing in Publication Data
A catalogue record for this title is available from the British Library

ISBN 1 86105 189 1

Printed by The Guernsey Press Ltd, Guernsey, Channel Islands

Preface

I regret that this collection of cartoons may not appeal to a number of my friends who regard the game with a certain disdain. I long ago established that as boys they attended a rugby-only school, and my oft-repeated claim that, compared with rugby, soccer is an art-form, almost balletic, leaves them quite un-impressed, even when I am forced to add the rider 'When played well, of course.'

Grist to their mill is added by the recent creeping commercialization of the game and the (fortunately receding) incidence of hooliganism. Neither of these regrettable tendencies seem to be affecting the enjoyment of the game by its millions of fans, nor their reactions to it, to which I too have always been especially sensitive.

My affection for soccer dates from boyhood when I once found myself in goal during a lunchtime scratch game in the school's concrete playground. The goal-posts were improvised from the uprights of the brick archways supporting the assembly hall above. Our House (and Geography) master happened to pass by just at the moment I accidentally, and theatrically, blocked a shot at goal. To the consternation of us all he announced my selection to play as goalkeeper in the next House match on the school's playing fields.

I have a memory block as to my subsequent prowess on a real grass pitch, except for a barbed comment from our team captain that in his choice of goalkeeper our House master's grasp of the rudiments of soccer was roughly equal to his teaching of Geography.

I press hastily on to my later career as a cartoonist when, by virtue of a few soccer cartoons published in a Sunday newspaper, I cajoled their sports desk to arrange a Press card to allow me free entry into the hallowed gates of White Hart Lane, home to my then local and revered team, Tottenham Hotspur FC.

Driving sedately into the ground with my Press label proudly displayed on the windscreen, I heard one fan remarking to his mate, 'What does *he* press? Trousers?' Years later when my allegiance was transferred to Wycombe Wanderers, a Second Division team, near my present home, I witnessed another memorable incident. The ball had been kicked into touch during a game. A linesman had taken up position next to the player taking the throw-in. Raising the ball above his head, the player hesitated briefly to make a comment to the linesman. It seemed a bit of harmless banter as they both appeared to smile. But instantly, from 5,000 throats, came a spontaneous shout of 'Aye! Aye!' I shall not attempt here to try to analyse the layers of hidden meanings in such a comment. If it implied a hint of collusion, then to what end?

Certainly as a purely verbal joke it cannot be translated usefully into cartoon form. But I hope I have managed to capture a good deal of the special and to me cherished humour of the soccer fan in the cartoons in this collection.

My thanks go to a fellow traveller, Graham Barnes, and to my son, Ben, both soccer *aficionados* extraordinary, for their kind help and advice in its preparation.

David Langdon

What size is YOUR helmet, Fred?

No dear, HE'S the mascot. The one behind him
is the Captain...

Let me explain the rudiments of the game to
you new City owners of the Club. First,
there are eleven men on each side...

Now let's see whether we can't maintain this spirit of
friendly rivalry throughout the game, shall we?

Item 1, Wages bill... I do wish you chaps would
concentrate on the agenda...

You pay good money to see a game of soccer and you can
never bear to watch a penalty...

Stretcher bearer!...

That's what I don't like about soccer duty –
you don't see much of the game…

Say 'Please!'...

Do me a favour, mate – nip back and find
out who scored...

I'm afraid we're withdrawing our £3 million
offer for your no. 9...

Just given 'em a half-time pep talk, guv'.
Left 'em all in tears...

Shake. May I congratulate you for not disputing
my offside decision?

Just listen to the crowd's reaction when I call for a Fred Bloggs to return home as his wife's just delivered triplets...

Who was that old player of ours who always took
an offside kick from the proper spot? Gave up soccer
and went into the Church...

Used to be the old magic-sponge cure;
these days they do ruddy eye-tests…

Quick! Hide! I always know when
your dad's team lost...

He still disputes the penalty, so go ahead
and take a shot at the empty goal...

I know. I know. I'm always a Good Ref
when my decisions happen to go your way...

Delicate creatures, today's goalkeepers. You used to be able to bundle 'em WITH the ball into the net and no foul...

Would you be kind enough to remind the penalty-taker
that this is a pre-season friendly?

nds, Ref. I used to play a lot of rugger...

For Pete's SAKE, man' don't let the ot
praying for a game...

Not a dicky bird from Passport Control. No 'Welcome to
La Belle France', or whatever…

Would you mind!
Your job is just to THROW the ball to me...

Sorry, mate – I was watching the game...

Got away with 100 lines – I must not say nasty things to
referees in the future...

NOW tell me women soccer players aren't
as brave as men...

What worries me is who's going to silver polish this
for a whole year...

That won't do HIS morale much good…

Sorry. This ball is perfectly sound, and certainly no excuse
for letting in that dreadful goal...

You notice when the home team scored the goal went up
immediately. We've just scored and it's taking ages...

Smashing pair of boots, mate. I'll have 'em when
you've done with 'em...

That's all we need, one dud bulb and the whole ruddy
crowd yells 'Shove a bob in the meter!'

Nothing in life can be more depressing than a 150-mile
drive home from an away-game defeat...

Right. Okay. Here's the gloves. YOU have a go!

Shout what you like, mate, but always add
'Pardon my French'...

Okay, sir. Please yourself. *I* say we're playing away today...

Okay, chaps. Stand by for an early mass exit. The home
side's five-nil down already...

Miserable old git. Keeps saying the only thing wrong with
our smashing new stand is it faces the pitch...

No, not a family bereavement. His local team's
been relegated...

Doesn't say much for a team if it does a lap of honour just for being given a corner...

I've been learning stuff like 'Where's your white stick,
Ref?' in French...

Before we kick off, Ref, are you quite sure this ball's not been made by Far Eastern child labour?

To make up for your appalling first half performance, I
suggest you spend the next 15 minutes replacing divots...

Won't exactly be a Guard of Honour. Not after the two
penalties I gave against the home side...

No! Please. Last time you jumped on me for scoring,
I was on the bench for a month with a back injury...

Sorry, guv'. I'm too whacked to play. I'm worn out after running up and down the touchline with the other subs...

Makes the 50 quid I spent on my replica shirt
worth it when I hear a young lad ask his dad what
position I play in..?

Isn't there any way you can warn the Ref that if he lets the
other side score in injury time he'll be lynched?...

Bit of a stickler this Ref, measuring the exact
10 yards with a surveyor's tape...

Poor lad's kissing the ground because he's grateful for
getting off the sub's bench...

Dad, you go on about us playing the Four–Four–Two
formation. Shouldn't it really be the
ONE–Four–Four–Two formation?

Remember what the gaffer says – 'Always LOOK like
you've a cunning plan for a free kick, even if you haven't…'

If *this* isn't shirt-tugging, Ref, what is?

Ask him the name of the Prime Minister and he hasn't a clue, but ask him who won the Cup Final in 1921 ...

Before we go on air with this pre-match interview could you please avoid 'If we score more goals than they do then we'll win...'

Wouldn't put it past the French to bring back the old
guillotine just for us...

Sorry. We're not into half-time scores...

Three-nil down already. And if anyone says 'It's a game of
two halves' I'll throttle him...

A fiver if you promise to destroy the negative...

Aren't you the chap who after last season's performance
swore you wouldn't be seen dead here again?

Oh come on, Ref! Half-time's up. Remember the old saying
– 'Sticks and stones may break my bones but words will
never hurt me'...

D'you know what they've got the ruddy cheek
to charge for a season ticket these days?

He's one of these ball-boys, dear, like what they have at
Wimbledon tennis...

Sorry, chaps. By 'Sheep' and 'Goats' I meant separating
home and away suppporters...

Just kick it back over the stand, dear,
so they can carry on with their game...

I've a spare Valium, if you want one...

I'm not keen on this idea of a one-minute's silence when
they've lost their last away game...

And this sign from the bench means 'THINK,
you stupid oaf'...

Right, I'll buy you the new, expensive junior supporters' strip, provided you don't let the lads at school then persuade you to follow Man United...

You're a non-league team, and with an average gate of 200
you're worried about a pitch invasion?

They've a lady physio. Blimey, our lads would be dropping
like flies with phoney injuries if WE had one...

Oh, good grief! Not soccer AGAIN?!!

To help communication between team members, this
young lady from the LEA has details of evening classes in
French, Italian, Spanish, German, etc...

I hope they get their wives to shove their exchange shirts
straight into the wash as soon as they get home...

I personally wouldn't have given all those millions
for him, would YOU?

Never mind, mate, the early bath is always the cleanest...

How is it that the visiting side is ALWAYS
taller and burlier than our lot?...

The Ref hasn't spotted your offside flag. Why don't you
each have a ruddy mobile phone?

Officially they call him 'Assistant Referee', but to me he'll
always be a stupid old Lino...

Be fair. Let me take this corner kick first, and THEN
you can shout 'What a waste!'

I knew the moment I bought you that replica kit you'd nag
to join our Premier Division Youth Team...

Just mention some of our players' wages and I bet you a quid he'll tell you how much the England team were paid for winning the World Cup in 1966...

Looks like those clamouring for the return of all-standing
terraces have found their own solution…

Dad, how do the crowd know the Ref's a w—r?